DASH DIET COOKBOOK FOR BEGINNERS

Quick Recipes for Flavorful & Healthy Meals.
Surprise Yourself with Healthy Cooking Journey.

Samuel Hayes

TABLE OF CONTENTS

Introduction

The DASH diet takes a novel approach since it teaches sustainable, simple-to-maintain eating patterns that are scientifically developed to help you reach your health goals without requiring you to give up delicious food. The DASH diet emphasizes simple alterations to your current diet in order to modify your eating habits to better suit your physical well-being, as opposed to following rigorous rules and restrictions and forcing you to give up the foods you love to cook. Fad diets may promise rapid weight loss, but in the long run, they rarely deliver. But the DASH diet works in a short amount of time and is easy to keep up with. It is up to you to find what you like and what works for you using the DASH diet's guidelines; there is no one proper way to follow the DASH diet. You'll be more aware of what you need to include in your meals and what can be left out when you start paying attention to what you're actually putting in your body and how you can make modest modifications where you find harmful tendencies.

The DASH diet differs from other popular diets in that it prioritizes heart health over weight loss. Focusing on lowering blood pressure has beneficial effects on overall health. As someone who has never been in particularly good health, the DASH diet initially appealed to me as a means to improve my overall well-being. However, I was unable to pin down the precise reason why I was never in top form. My friend told me she had recently read about the link between the excessive salt intake of Americans and serious health issues, including heart failure and stroke. The possibility that my high salt consumption was a major contributor to my less-than-ideal health status had never occurred to me before. With more research, I found That the more I considered the DASH diet, the more attractive it seemed. I am following the DASH diet, and if you want to avoid high blood pressure, so should you.

Chapter 1 The DASH Diet

Dietary Approaches to Stop Hypertension (DASH): A Heart-Healthy Plan

DASH refers to the Dietary Approaches to Stop Hypertension plan. DASH stands for Dietary Approaches to Stop Hypertension, and it is a healthy eating strategy to lower blood pressure (Hypertension). Foods high in potassium, calcium, and magnesium are part of the DASH diet. Blood pressure is lowered by these foods. High-sodium, high-saturated-fat, and high-added-sugar foods are avoided. Blood pressure can be lowered with the DASH diet in as little as two weeks. Blood levels of low-density lipoprotein ("bad" cholesterol) can also be lowered by changing one's diet. Both high blood pressure and high levels of "bad" LDL cholesterol can increase the risk of cardiovascular disease and stroke.

DASH diet and sodium

The average American diet, in contrast to the DASH diet, may contain as much as 3,400 milligrams (mg) of sodium per day. Sodium intake is restricted to 2,300 milligrams per day on the DASH diet. Following the Dietary Guidelines for Americans' guideline to consume fewer than 2,300 milligrams of sodium daily, this dish is OK. A teaspoon of regular salt contains about that much sodium. Sodium intake is limited to 1,500 milligrams per day on the DASH-L plan. Find the eating plan that works best for you and stick to it. Consult your doctor if you are unsure of your optimal salt intake.

DASH diet: What to eat

The DASH eating plan is a balanced and adaptable eating plan that can help you develop a lifetime of heart-healthy eating habits. A majority of the ingredients may be bought at a typical grocery store. Plant-based foods and whole grains are featured heavily in the DASH diet. Dairy products, fish, chicken, legumes, and nuts that are low in fat or fat-free are all part of this category. Saturated fat-rich foods like red meat and full-fat dairy are restricted. Foods that should be prioritized when following the DASH diet are those that are:

- Rich in magnesium, potassium, calcium, fiber, and protein
- Low in saturated fat
- Low in sodium

Guidelines for the DASH diet

The DASH eating plan includes weekly and daily dietary guidelines. Your calorie needs will determine how many servings you should consume. For a DASH diet of 2,000 calories per day, here are the serving sizes that are recommended:

- **Grains: 6 to 8 servings a day.** One slice of bread, one ounce of dry cereal, or half a cup of cooked rice or pasta all count as one serving.
- **Vegetables: 4 to 5 servings a day.** One cup of raw leafy greens, 1/2 cup of chopped raw or cooked vegetables, or 1/2 cup of vegetable juice equals one serving.
- **Fruits: 4 to 5 servings a day.** One medium-sized piece of fruit, half a cup of frozen, fresh, or canned fruit, or half a cup of fruit juice constitutes one serving.
- **Dairy products, 2–3 servings per day, fat-free or low-fat.** One serving of milk, yogurt, and cheese is 1 cup and 1 1/2 ounces, respectively.
- **The daily intake of lean meats, poultry, and fish should be limited to no more than six 1-ounce servings.** Meat, poultry, and fish that are each 1 ounce cooked, as well as a single egg, make up a single serving.
- **There should be four or five servings of nuts, seeds, and legumes in your weekly diet.** 1/2 cup of cooked legumes, 2 tablespoons of peanut butter, 2 tablespoons of nuts, or 1/3 cup of nuts and seeds constitute one serving (dried beans or peas).
- **Two or three servings of oils and fats daily are recommended.** 1 serving equals 1 tsp vegetable oil, 1 tsp soft margarine, 1 tbsp mayonnaise, or 2 tbsp salad dressing.
- **Limit yourself to no more than 5 servings of sugary foods and beverages per week.** One cup of lemonade, half a cup of sorbet, or one tablespoon of sugar constitutes one serving.

Take aim at sodium

DASH diet staples are naturally low in sodium because of their focus on the whole, plant-based foods. If you want to decrease your sodium intake, the DASH diet is a good place to start. Additional sodium reduction is possible by:

- Replace salt with sodium-free spices or seasonings.
- Avoid adding salt to cooked grains like rice, pasta, and cereal.
- Opting for unadorned fresh, frozen, or canned veggies
- Getting skinless poultry, fish, and lean cuts of meat that are either fresh or frozen
- You can cut down on salt by reading food labels and choosing options with less salt or none at all.

You may find that the flavor of foods changes as you reduce your consumption of processed and high-sodium options. Some people need time to adjust their taste buds. If it does, though, you might find that the DASH diet is the one you gravitate toward in the long run.

Chapter 2 Breakfast

SWEET AVOCADO SMOOTHIE

Serves: 2 | Time: 5 Minutes

Ingredients:

- 2 Cups Ice Cubes
- 1 Teaspoon Vanilla Extract, Pure
- 1 ½ Teaspoons Granulated Stevia
- 1 ½ Cups Milk, Nonfat
- 1 ½ Cups Peaches, Frozen
- 1 Cup Vanilla Greek Yogurt
- 1 Tablespoon Flaxseed, Ground
- 1 Avocado, Peeled & Pitted

Directions:

1. Blend everything and serve.

Nutrition Info:

- Calories: 323
- Protein: 21 Grams
- Fat: 15 Grams
- Carbs: 32 Grams
- Sodium: 142 mg
- Cholesterol: 9 mg

CINNAMON APPLE OVERNIGHT OATS

Serves: 2 | Time: 8 Hours 15 Minutes

Ingredients:

- 1 Cup Old Fashioned Rolled Oats
- 2 Tablespoons Chia Seeds
- 1¼ Cup Milk, Nonfat
- ½ Tablespoon Ground Cinnamon
- 2 Teaspoons Honey, Raw
- ½ Teaspoon Vanilla Extract, Pure
- Dash Sea Salt
- 1 Apple, Diced

Directions:

1. Mason jars should be used to store your chia seeds, oats, cinnamon, milk, honey, vanilla extract, and salt. Cover each container with its lid, then give it a good shake, so the ingredients are evenly distributed.
2. After removing the lids, divide your sliced apples in half and place one-half of each serving into each jar. Cinnamon should be sprinkled on top. After replacing the lids on the jars, place them in the refrigerator to chill overnight.

Nutrition Info:

- Calories: 339
- Carbs: 60 Grams
- Protein: 13 Grams
- Fat: 8 Grams
- Sodium: 66 mg
- Cholesterol: 3 mg

BLUEBERRY MUFFINS

Serves: 12 | Time: 45 Minutes

Ingredients:

- 1 ¼ Cup Whole Wheat Flour
- ½ Cup Old Fashioned Rolled Oats
- 1 Teaspoon Baking Soda
- 1 Teaspoon Baking Powder
- ¼ Teaspoon Ground Cinnamon
- ¼ Teaspoon Sea Salt, Fine
- ¼ Cup Olive Oil
- ¼ Cup Dark Brown Sugar
- 2/3 Cup Milk
- 1 Cup Blueberries, Fresh or Frozen
- 8 Medjool Dates, Pitted & Chopped
- 1Teaspoon Vanilla Extract, Pure
- 2Eggs, Large

Directions:

1. To begin, set your oven temperature to 350 degrees, and then line a muffin tin with paper liners. Take a bowl, add your baking soda, oats, flour, baking powder, cinnamon, and salt, and whisk everything until they are thoroughly blended.
2. Take out a second bowl and, using the first bowl, whisk the olive oil and brown sugar together in the second bowl until the mixture becomes frothy. After thoroughly beating the mixture before adding the eggs one at a time, add the milk and vanilla extract and continue to whisk until smooth. Beat thoroughly to combine.
3. Mix together the dry and wet ingredients thoroughly after adding the flour mixture. After dividing the mixture between the muffin cups in an even manner, put them in the oven for twenty-five minutes.

Nutrition Info:

- Calories: 180
- Protein: 4 Grams
- Fat: 6 Grams
- Carbs: 30 Grams
- Sodium: 172 mg
- Cholesterol: 35 mg

YOGURT AND BANANA MUFFINS

Serves: 4 | Time: 40 Minutes

Ingredients:

- 3 Bananas, Large & Mashed
- 1 Teaspoon Baking Soda
- 1 Cup Old Fashioned Rolled Oats
- 2 Tablespoons Flaxseed, Ground
- 1 Cup Whole Wheat Flour
- ¼ Cup Applesauce, Unsweetened
- ½ Cup Plain Yogurt
- ¼ Cup Brown Sugar
- 2 Teaspoons Vanilla Extract, Pure

Directions:

1. To begin, set the temperature in the oven to 355 degrees, and then take out a muffin tray. First, grease the surface, and then get a bowl ready. In a bowl, combine the ground flaxseed, oats, baking soda, and flour.
2. First, mash up the banana, and then stir in the sugar, vanilla extract, yogurt, and apple sauce. Add in your oats mixture while stirring, making sure that everything is thoroughly blended. It is acceptable for there to be lumps in it.
3. Bake for 25 minutes after dividing the mixture among many muffin tins. They should be served hot.

Nutrition Info:

- Calories: 316
- Sodium: 469 mg
- Cholesterol: 43 mg
- Protein: 11.2 Grams
- Fat: 14.5 Grams
- Carbs: 36.8 Grams

BERRY QUINOA BOWLS

Serves: 2 | Time: 35 Minutes

Ingredients:

- 1 Small Peach, Sliced
- 2/3 + ¾ Cup Milk, Low Fat
- 1/3 Cup Uncooked Quinoa, Rinsed Well
- ½ Teaspoon Vanilla Extract, Pure
- 2 Teaspoons Brown Sugar
- 14 Blueberries
- 2 Teaspoons Honey, Raw
- 12 Raspberries

Directions:

1. It is recommended that you bring your quinoa, vanilla extract, brown sugar, and 2/3 cup of milk to a boil for five minutes before decreasing the heat to a simmer.

2. Prepare for twenty minutes at medium heat. After preheating a grill pan that has been coated and placing it over a medium heat source, add your peaches and allow them to cook for one minute on each side. You should heat the remaining three-quarters of a cup of milk in the microwave.

3. Prepare the quinoa by cooking it with a little bit of milk, some berries, and some grilled peaches. Before serving, be sure to sprinkle it with honey.

Nutrition Info:

- Calories: 435
- Protein: 9.2 Grams
- Fat: 13.7 Grams
- Carbs: 24.9 Grams
- Sodium: 141 mg
- Cholesterol: 78 mg

PINEAPPLE GREEN SMOOTHIE

Serves: 2 | Time: 5 Minutes

Ingredients:

- 1 ¼ Cups Orange Juice
- ½ Cup Greek Yogurt, Plain
- 1 Cup Spinach, Fresh
- 1 Cup Pineapple, Frozen & Chunked
- 1 Cup Mango, Frozen & Chunked
- 1 Tablespoon Ground Flaxseed
- 1 Teaspoon Granulated Stevia

Directions:

1. To begin, combine all of the ingredients in a blender and process until smooth. Serve chilled.

Nutrition Info:

- Calories: 213
- Protein: 9 Grams
- Fat: 2 Grams
- Carbs: 43 Grams
- Sodium: 44 mg
- Cholesterol: 2.5 mg

PEANUT BUTTER AND BANANA SMOOTHIE

Serves: 1 | Time: 5 Minutes

Ingredients:

- 1 Cup Milk, Nonfat
- 1 Tablespoon Peanut Butter, All Natural
- 1 Banana, Frozen & Sliced

Directions:

1. To begin, combine all of the ingredients in a blender and process until smooth.

Nutrition Info:

- Calories: 146
- Protein: 1.1 Grams
- Fat: 5.5 Grams
- Carbs: 1.8 Grams
- Sodium: 38 mg

MUSHROOM FRITTATA

Serves: 4 | Time: 30 Minutes

Ingredients:

- 4 Shallots, Chopped
- 1Tablespoons Butter
- 2Teaspoons parsley, Fresh & Diced
- ½ lb. Mushrooms, Fresh & Diced
- 3Eggs
- 1 Teaspoon Thyme
- 5 Egg Whites
- ¼ Teaspoon Black Pepper
- 1 Tablespoon Half & Half, Fat-Free
- ¼ Cup Parmesan Cheese, Grated

Directions:

1. First, bring a skillet to the table, and then preheat the oven to 350 degrees. Grease it with butter and let it melt while it's being heated over a medium flame. When the butter has reached the desired temperature, stir in the shallots.

2. To achieve a golden brown color, continue cooking for approximately five minutes. Mix in your thyme, pepper, parsley, and mushrooms once you've stirred in your parsley. In a bowl, combine the eggs, egg whites, parmesan, and half-and-half, and then beat the mixture.
3. After pouring the mixture over the mushrooms, allow it to cook for an additional two minutes. Put the skillet in the oven. Bake it for fifteen minutes to finish the dish. Cut into slices and serve warm.

Nutrition Info:

- Calories: 391
- Protein: 7.6 Grams
- Fat: 12.8 Grams
- Carbs: 31.5 Grams
- Sodium: 32 mg
- Cholesterol: 112 mg

CHEESY OMELET

Serves: 4 | Time: 20 Minutes

Ingredients:

- 4 Eggs
- 4 Cups Broccoli Florets
- 1 Tablespoon Olive Oil
- 1 Cup Egg Whites
- ¼ Cup Cheddar, Reduced Fat
- ¼ Cup Romano, Grated
- ¼ Teaspoon Sea Salt, Fine
- ¼ Teaspoon Black Pepper
- Cooking Spray as Needed

Directions:

1. After preheating the oven to 350 degrees, steam the broccoli for five to seven minutes over boiling water. The oven should have been preheated to 350 degrees. It needs to

have a soft texture. After you have mashed the broccoli into little pieces, season it with salt and pepper, and then mix it with olive oil.

2. Get a muffin tin ready by spraying it with cooking spray before you get it out. Make sure that each cup has an equal amount of broccoli, and then get a bowl ready. Your eggs should have some salt, pepper, egg whites, and parmesan beaten into them in the bowl. After you have poured the batter over the broccoli, sprinkle some cheese on top. Wait two minutes after baking before serving at a warm temperature.

Nutrition Info:

- Calories: 427
- Protein: 7.5 Grams
- Fat: 8.6 Grams
- Carbs: 13 Grams
- Sodium: 282 mg
- Cholesterol: 4.2 Grams

GINGER CONGEE

Serves: 1 | Time: 1 Hour 10 Minutes

Ingredients:

- 1 Cup White Rice, Long Grain & Rinsed
- 7 Cups Chicken Stock
- 1 Inch Ginger, Peeled & Sliced Thin
- Green Onion, Sliced for Garnish Sesame Seed Oil to Garnish

Directions:

1. To begin, place your ginger, rice, and salt in a pot. Then bring it to a boil. Let it come to a boil. Then lower the heat to a simmer. After giving it a light stir, let it simmer for an hour without disturbing it.
2. It needs to have a thick and creamy consistency. Serve hot after decorating with a drizzle of sesame oil as a finishing touch.

Nutrition Info:

- Calories: 510
- protein: 13.5 Grams

- Carbs: 60.7 Grams
- Fat: 24.7 Grams
- Sodium: 840 mg
- Cholesterol: 0 mg

EGG MELTS

Serves: 2 | Time: 20 Minutes

Ingredients:

- 1 Teaspoon Olive oil
- 2 English Muffins, Whole Grain & Split
- 4 Scallions, Sliced Fine
- 8 Egg Whites, Whisked
- ¼ Teaspoon Sea Salt, Fine
- ¼ Teaspoon Black Pepper
- ½ Cup Swiss Cheese, Shredded & Reduced Fat
- ½ Cup Grape Tomatoes, Quartered

Directions:

1. After preheating the oven to broil, place the English muffins on a baking sheet, and then turn the oven to broil. Make sure that the side that was split is pointing upward. Cook under the broiler for two minutes. Around the perimeter, they should develop a golden color. Bring a frying pan to the table and coat it with oil.

2. It should be heated over medium heat for three minutes, and the scallions should be cooked. After beating your egg whites with some salt and pepper, pour them on top of your sliced scallions. Continue to cook for one more minute while stirring the pan gently.

3. Spread this on top of the muffins, and then top with the remaining scallions, cheese, and tomatoes, if you so wish. Continue broiling for an additional minute and a half to melt the cheese, then serve warm.

Nutrition Info:

- Calories: 212
- Protein: 5.3 Grams
- Fat: 3.9 Grams
- Carbs: 14.3 Grams
- Sodium: 135 mg
- Cholesterol: 0 mg

Chapter 3 Lunch

CHEESY BLACK BEAN WRAPS

Serves: 6 | Time: 15 Minutes

Ingredients:

- 2 Tablespoons Green Chili Peppers, Chopped
- 4 Green Onions, Diced
- 1 Tomato, Diced
- 1 Tablespoon Garlic, Chopped
- 6 Tortilla Wraps, Whole Grain & Fat-Free
- ¾ Cup Cheddar Cheese, Shredded
- ¾ Cup Salsa
- 1 ½ Cups Corn Kernels
- 3 Tablespoons Cilantro, Fresh & Chopped
- 1 ½ Cup Black Beans, Canned & Drained

Directions:

1. Place the chili peppers, corn, black beans, garlic, tomato, onion, and cilantro in a bowl and toss them all together. Heat the mixture in the microwave for one minute, then whisk

it for another half a minute after it has been heated. Place the two tortillas on a baking sheet and cover them with two paper towels.

2. Microwave on high for twenty seconds. To each of the tortillas that you have left, add a half cup of the bean mixture, two tablespoons of salsa, and two tablespoons of cheese after you have rewarmed the remaining tortillas in the same manner. Before serving, roll them up like a cigar.

Nutrition Info

- Calories: 341
- Protein: 19 Grams
- Fat: 11 Grams
- Carbs: 36.5 Grams
- Sodium: 141 mg
- Cholesterol: 0 mg

ARUGULA RISOTTO

Serves: 4 | Time: 25 Minutes

Ingredients:

- 1 Tablespoon Olive Oil
- ½ Cup Yellow Onion, Chopped
- 1 Cup Quinoa, Rinsed
- 1 Clove Garlic, Minced
- 2½ Cups Vegetable Stock, Low Sodium
- 2 Cups Arugula, Chopped & Stemmed
- 1 Carrot, Peeled & shredded
- ½ Cup Shiitake Mushrooms, Sliced
- ¼ Teaspoon Black Pepper
- ¼ Teaspoon Sea Salt, Fine
- ¼ Cup Parmesan Cheese, Grated

Directions:

1. Get a pot and put it on the stove at medium heat. This will heat up your oil. After the onions have been cooking for four minutes and have become more tender, add the garlic and quinoa to the pan.

2. Prepare for one minute. After stirring in the stock, bring the mixture to a boil. Lower the heat to maintain a simmer. Then continue cooking for another 12 minutes.

3. After a further two minutes of cooking, incorporate your arugula, mushrooms, and carrots into the dish. Before serving, sprinkle some salt, pepper, and cheese over the dish.

Nutrition Info

- Calories: 288
- Protein: 6 Grams
- Fat: 5 Grams
- Carbs: 28 Grams
- Sodium: 739 mg
- Cholesterol: 0.5 mg

VEGETARIAN STUFFED EGGPLANT

Serves: 2 | Time: 35 Minutes

Ingredients:

- 4 Ounces White Beans, Cooked
- 1 Tablespoon Olive Oil
- 1 cup Water
- 1 Eggplant
- ¼ Cup Onion, Chopped
- ½ Cup Bell Pepper, Chopped
- 1 Cup Canned Tomatoes, Unsalted
- ¼ Cup Tomato Liquid
- ¼ Cup Celery, Chopped
- 1 Cup Mushrooms, Fresh & Sliced
- ¾ Cup Breadcrumbs, Whole Wheat
- Black Pepper to Taste

Directions:

1. Preheat the oven to 350 degrees. Then spray a baking dish with cooking spray and place it in the oven. Remove the stem and cut the eggplant in half lengthwise after trimming it. Using a spoon, remove the pulp, and you should be left with a shell that is about a half-centimeter thick.

2. Put the shells in the dish with the cut side facing up so that they can bake. To begin, pour the water into the bottom of the dish. Next, cut the eggplant pulp into cubes and set them aside. Start heating the oil in a cast-iron skillet over medium heat.

3. Combine the chopped peppers, chopped eggplants, and chopped onions with the chopped celery, mushrooms, tomatoes, and tomato juice in a mixing bowl. After ten minutes of cooking over a low heat setting, whisk in your bread crumbs, beans, and ground black pepper. Continue cooking. The mixture should be divided between the eggshells. Bake for one minute and fifteen seconds with the foil on top. To be served hot.

Nutrition Info

- Calories: 334
- Protein: 26 Grams
- Fat: 10 Grams
- Carbs: 35 Grams
- Sodium: 142 mg
- Cholesterol: 162 mg

VEGETABLE TACOS

Serves: 4 | Time: 30 Minutes

Ingredients:

- 1 Tablespoon Olive Oil
- 1 Cup Red Onion, Chopped
- 1 Cup Yellow Summer Squash, Diced
- 1 Cup Green Zucchini, Diced
- 3Cloves Garlic, Minced
- 4Tomatoes, Seeded& Chopped
- 1 Jalapeno Chili, Seeded & Chopped
- 1 Cup Corn Kernels, Fresh
- 1 Cup Pinto Beans, Canned, Rinsed & Drained
- ½ Cup Cilantro, Fresh & Chopped
- 8 Corn Tortillas
- ½ Cup Smoke Flavored Salsa

Directions:

1. Take out a saucepan, add your olive oil to it, and then add your onion while stirring it over medium heat. Cook until tender. After adding the zucchini and squash, continue to simmer for an additional five minutes.
2. Mix in the minced garlic, canned beans, diced tomatoes, diced jalapenos, and corn. Continue cooking for another five minutes, then toss in your cilantro and remove the skillet from the heat once it has cooled slightly. Warm each tortilla by cooking it for twenty seconds on each side in a skillet that does not stick.
3. Put the tortillas on a serving platter, and then use a spoon to fill each one with the veggie mixture. Roll it up, then spread it with salsa and serve.

Nutrition Info

- Calories: 310
- Protein: 10 Grams
- Fat: 6 Grams
- Carbs: 54 Grams
- Sodium: 97 mg
- Cholesterol: 20 mg

TUSCAN STEW

Serves: 6 | Time: 1 Hour 40 Minutes

Ingredients:

<u>Croutons:</u>

- 1 Tablespoon Olive Oil
- 1Slice Bread, Whole Grain & Cubed
- 2Cloves Garlic, Quartered

<u>Soup:</u>

- 1 Bay Leaf
- 2 Cups White Beans, Soaked Overnight & Drained
- 6 Cups Water
- ½ Teaspoon Sea Salt, Divided
- 1 Cup Yellow Onion, Chopped
- 2 Tablespoons Olive Oil
- 3 Carrots, Peeled & Chopped

- 6 Cloves Garlic, Chopped
- ¼ Teaspoon Ground Black Pepper
- 1 Tablespoon Rosemary, Fresh & Chopped
- 1 ½ Cups Vegetable Stock

Directions:

1. After adding your oil to a pan and causing it to heat up, proceed to sauté your garlic for one minute. It ought to take on an aromatic quality. Before taking the garlic from the oil, give it 10 minutes to settle, after which you can do so. After you've brought the pan in which the oil is stored back up to temperature, add the cubes of bread. Wait five minutes before serving. They ought to have a golden color, after which you should put them to the side.

2. In the pot, combine the salt, water, bay leaf, and white beans. Bring to a boil over high heat. Then reduce the heat to maintain a simmer. Cooking the beans for an hour to an hour and ten minutes with the lid on is recommended. They should have a toothsome consistency. After they have finished cooking, drain the beans but set aside a half cup of the cooking liquid. Toss out the bay leaf, then place the beans in a basin to cool down. Combine the liquid that was reserved with a half cup of the beans, then bring it back to a boil. After creating a paste with a fork, place the pot on the burner and continue mashing the ingredients.

3. The pot should be used to heat up the oil. Include your chopped onions and carrots in the dish. After seven minutes of cooking, add the garlic and continue to cook for one minute more. In a large bowl, combine the rosemary, salt, pepper, bean mixture, and stock. First, let it get to a rolling boil. Then turn the heat down so that it can simmer. It should be allowed to simmer for five minutes before the croutons are added. Add sprigs of rosemary as a garnish, and then dig in!

Nutrition Info

- Calories: 307
- Protein: 16 Grams
- Fat: 7 Grams
- Carbs: 45 Grams
- Sodium: 463 mg
- Cholesterol: 68 mg

TENDERLOIN FAJITAS

Serves: 8 | Time: 35 Minutes

Ingredients:

- ¼ Teaspoon Garlic Powder
- ¼ Teaspoon Ground Coriander
- 1 Tablespoon Chili Powder
- ½ Teaspoon Paprika
- ½ Teaspoon Oregano
- 1 lb. Pork Tenderloin, Sliced into Strips
- 8 Flour Tortillas, Whole Wheat & Warned
- 1 Small Onion, Sliced
- ½ Cup Cheddar Cheese, Shredded
- 4 Tomatoes, Diced
- 1 Cup Salsa
- 4 Cups Lettuce, Shredded

Directions:

1. After preheating the grill to 400 degrees, combine the coriander, garlic, oregano, and paprika in a bowl before adding the paprika. Add the pork pieces and make sure they are evenly covered before adding them to the pan.
2. Place the pork and onions that you intend to cook on a grilling grate and grill them for five minutes on each side. Stuff the tortillas with the mixture, then top each one with a half cup of shredded lettuce, two teaspoons of salsa, a tablespoon of tomatoes, and a tablespoon of cheese.
3. Before serving heated tortillas, make sure to fold them.

Nutrition Info

- Calories: 250
- Protein: 44 Grams
- Fat: 9.8 Grams
- Carbs: 21.1 Grams
- Sodium: 671 mg
- Cholesterol: 22 mg

PEANUT SAUCE CHICKEN PASTA

Serves: 4 | Time: 30 Minutes

Ingredients:

- 2 Teaspoons Olive Oil
- Cilantro, Fresh & Chopped
- 6 Ounces Spaghetti, Whole Wheat
- 10 Ounces Snap Peas, Fresh & Trimmed & Sliced into Strips
- 2 Cups Carrots, Julienned
- 2Cups Chicken, Cooked & Shredded
- 1 Cup Thai Peanut Sauce
- 1 Cucumber, Halved Lengthwise & Sliced Diagonally

Directions:

1. To begin, the spaghetti should be cooked according to the directions on the package. The noodles should be rinsed in cold water after draining. Warm up your oiled and greased skillet over a medium heat setting. When it reaches the desired temperature, add your snap peas and carrots.

2. After eight minutes of cooking, stir in your spaghetti, chicken, and peanut sauce. Continue cooking for two more minutes. To finish, garnish with cucumber and cilantro after giving everything a good toss.

Nutrition Info

- Calories: 403
- Protein: 31 Grams
- Fat: 15 Grams
- Carbs: 43 Grams
- Sodium: 432 mg
- Cholesterol: 42 mg

CHICKEN CHERRY WRAPS

Serves: 4 | Time: 20 Minutes

Ingredients:

- ¼ Teaspoon Sea Salt, Fine
- ¼ Teaspoon Black Pepper
- 2 Teaspoons Olive oil
- ¾ lb. Chicken Breasts, Boneless & Cubed
- 1 Teaspoon Ginger, Ground
- 1 ½ Cups Carrots, Shredded
- 1 ¼ Cup Sweet Cherries, Fresh, Pitted & Chopped
- 4 Green Onions, Chopped
- 2 Tablespoons Rice Vinegar
- 1/3 Cup Almonds, Chopped Roughly
- 2 Tablespoons Rice Vinegar
- 2 Tablespoons Teriyaki Sauce, Low Sodium
- 1 Tablespoon Honey Raw
- 8 Large Lettuce Leaves

Directions:

1. Ginger, salt, and pepper should be used to season your chicken. Take out a skillet, set it over a heat source of medium intensity, and pour in the oil. Cook the chicken for five minutes once the oil has reached the desired temperature. Include your almonds, cherries, green onions, and carrots in the mix.

2. After ensuring that the chicken is fully cooked through, add in your vinegar, teriyaki, and honey before making sure that everything is thoroughly combined. To serve, spread this on individual lettuce leaves.

Nutrition Info

- Calories: 257
- Protein: 21 Grams
- Fat: 10 Grams
- Carbs: 21 Grams
- Sodium: 381 mg
- Cholesterol: 47 mg

EASY BARLEY SOUP

Serves: 4 | Time: 30 Minutes

Ingredients:

- 1 Tablespoon Olive Oil
- 1 Onion, Chopped
- 5Carrots, Chopped
- 2/3 Cup Barley, Quick Cooking
- 6Cups Chicken Broth, Reduced Sodium
- ½ Teaspoon Black Pepper
- 2 Cups Baby Spinach, Fresh
- 2 Cups Turkey Breast, Cooked & Cubed

Directions:

1. To begin, get a saucepan and heat the oil in it over medium-high heat in the pan. After stirring in the carrots and onion, cook them for five minutes in the skillet before adding the barley and the broth.

2. First, bring it up to a boil. Then reduce the heat to a low simmer. Prepare for fifteen minutes at medium heat. Mix in the pepper, spinach, and turkey to your dish. Just before serving, mix thoroughly.

Nutrition Info

- Calories: 208
- Protein: 21 Grams
- Fat: 4 Grams
- Carbs: 23 Grams
- Sodium: 662 mg
- Cholesterol: 37 mg

CURRY CHICKEN POCKETS

Serves: 4 | Time: 35 Minutes

Ingredients:

- 2 Cups Chicken, Cooked & Chopped
- ½ Cup Celery, Chopped
- 1/3 Cup Ricotta Cheese, Part Skim
- 1/ Cup Carrot, Shredded
- 1 Teaspoon Curry Powder
- 1 Tablespoon Apricot Preserved
- 10 Ounces Refrigerated Pizza Dough
- ¼ Teaspoon Sea Salt
- ¼ Teaspoon Ground Cinnamon

Directions:

1. Combine the chicken, celery, carrots, ricotta, preserves, cinnamon, salt, and curry powder in a mixing bowl. After it has been spread out, the pizza dough should be cut into six squares of equal size.

2. After dividing your mixture among them, fold the four corners of each square towards the center and pinch them together. Place them on the baking sheet. Bake them for fifteen minutes at 375 degrees. They need to achieve a golden-brown color after they have had time to cool; serve them warm.

Nutrition Info

- Calories: 415
- Protein: 31.2 Grams
- Fat: 32.7 Grams
- Carbs: 14.7 Grams
- Sodium: 277 mg
- Cholesterol: 4.1 mg

FAJITA STYLE CHILI

Serves: 4 | Time: 5 Hours 10 Minutes

Ingredients:

- 1 Teaspoon Fajita Seasoning
- 1 Tablespoon Chili Powder
- 2 lbs. Chicken Breasts, Boneless & Cubed
- ½ Teaspoon Cumin, Ground
- 2 Cloves Garlic, Minced
- Nonstick Cooking Spray as Needed
- 2 Cans (14.5 Ounces Each) Tomatoes, Diced
- ½ Green Bell Pepper, Julienned
- ½ Red Bell Pepper, Julienned
- ½ Yellow Bell Pepper, Julienned
- ½ Onion, Sliced
- 15 Ounces White Kidney Beans, Rinsed & Drained (Canned)

- 3 Tablespoons Sour Cream
- 3 Tablespoon Cheddar Cheese, Shredded & Reduced Fat
- 3 Tablespoons Guacamole

Directions:

1. In a mixing bowl, combine fajita seasoning, garlic, cumin, and chili powder with your chicken. Heat a skillet with cooking spray over medium heat.
2. After adding the chicken, continue to cook it until it is a deep golden color. It should then be placed in a slow cooker, after which the tomatoes, along with their juices and vegetables, and beans, should be added.
3. Cook on low heat with the lid on for five hours. Before serving warm, top each portion with guacamole, cheese, and sour cream as desired.

Nutrition Info

- Calories: 495
- Protein: 67.4 Grams
- Fat: 11.5 Grams
- Carbs: 10.2 Grams
- Sodium: 212 mg
- Cholesterol: 183 mg

FUN FAJITA WRAPS

Serves: 4 | Time: 20 Minutes

Ingredients:

- Nonstick Cooking Spray
- ¼ Teaspoon Garlic Powder
- ½ Teaspoon Chili Powder
- 12 Ounces of Chicken Breasts, Skinless & Sliced into Strips
- 1 Green Sweet Pepper, Seeded & Sliced into Strips
- 2 Tortilla, 10 Inches & Whole Wheat
- 2 Tablespoons Ranch Salad Dressing, Reduced Calorie
- ½ Cup Salsa
- 1/3 Cup Cheddar Cheese, Shredded & Reduced Fat

Directions:

1. Add some chili powder and garlic powder to your chicken strips, and mix well. Warm up a skillet and spray it with some cooking spray before using it. Place it on the stovetop over medium heat and add the chicken and peppers.

2. Prepare for six minutes at high heat. Toss in the salad dressing, then divide the mixture evenly among the tortillas. After spreading the tortilla with salsa and cheese, roll it up and then cut it in half lengthwise. To be served hot.

Nutrition Info

- Calories: 245
- Protein: 38.5 Grams
- Fat: 16.4 Grams
- Carbs: 8.7 Grams
- Sodium: 471 mg
- Cholesterol: 143 mg

CLASSIC CHICKEN NOODLE SOUP

Serves: 4 | Time: 30 Minutes

Ingredients:

- 1 Teaspoon Olive Oil
- 1 Cup Onion, Chopped
- 3 Cloves Garlic, Minced
- 1 Cup Celery, Chopped
- 1 Cup Carrots, Sliced & Peeled
- 4 Cups Chicken Broth
- 4 Ounces Linguini, Dried & Broken
- 1Cup Chicken Breast, Cooked & Chopped
- 2Tablespoons Parsley, Fresh

Directions:

1. Put a saucepan over medium heat, and heat up your oil. Stir in your onion and garlic, cooking until softened.

2. Add your celery and carrots. Cook for three minutes before adding your broth. Allow it to come to a boil before reducing it to a simmer. Cook for five minutes before adding in your linguini.
3. Bring it to a boil and lower the heat to simmer. Cook for ten more minutes.
4. Add in your parsley and chicken, and then cook until heated all the way through. Serve warm.

Nutrition Info

- Calories: 381
- Protein: 25.3 Grams
- Fat: 12.9 Grams
- Carbs: 9.7 Grams
- Sodium: 480 mg
- Cholesterol: 37 mg

Chapter 4 Dinner

FENNEL SAUCE TENDERLOIN

Serves: 4 | Time: 35 Minutes

Ingredients:

- Fennel Bulb, Cored & Sliced
- Sweet Onion, Sliced
- ½ Cup Dry White Wine
- Teaspoon Fennel Seeds
- 4 Pork Tenderloin Fillets
- Tablespoons Olive Oil
- 12 Ounces Chicken Broth, Low Sodium
- Fennel Fronds for Garnish Orange Slices for Garnish

Directions:

1. To achieve a more uniform thickness throughout the pork tenderloin, lay it out between two sheets of paper and pound it with a mallet. When the skillet is hot, add the oil to the pan. Cook the fennel seeds for three minutes in the pot by placing them over a heat source of medium intensity.

2. The pork should be added to the pan and given an additional three minutes of cooking time per side. After placing it to the side, transfer the pork to a dish, and then add the fennel and the onion to the tray. Prepare the vegetables for five minutes, and then move them to the side of the pan.

3. Place the wine and broth in the pot, then turn the heat up to high. Then bring it to a boil. Continue cooking until about half of the liquid is left. Place the pork back into the skillet and continue to cook it for another five minutes. Mix in your onion mixture while maintaining the lid. Continue to cook for an additional two minutes, then serve warm.

Nutrition Info

- Calories: 276
- Protein: 23.4 Grams
- Fat: 24 Grams
- Carbs: 14 Grams
- Sodium: 647 mg
- Cholesterol: 49 mg

BEEFY FENNEL STEW

Serves: 4 | Time: 1 Hour 40 Minutes

Ingredients:

- 1lb. Lean Beef, Boneless & Cubed
- 2Tablespoons Olive Oil
- ½ Fennel Bulb, Sliced
- 3Tablespoons All Purpose Flour
- 3 Shallots, Large & Chopped
- ¾ Teaspoon Black Pepper, Divided
- 2 Thyme Sprigs, Fresh
- Bay Leaf
- ½ Cup Red Wine
- 3Cups Vegetable Stock
- 4Carrots, Peeled & Sliced into 1 Inch Pieces
- 4 White Potatoes, Large & Cubed
- 18 Small Boiling Onions, Halved
- 1/3 Cup Flat Leaf Parsley, Fresh & Chopped

- Portobello Mushrooms, Chopped

Directions:

1. Take your flour and place it in a jar that is not very deep. Run the meat cubes through it, then shake off any extra flour that is left on them. Take out a saucepan, pour in your oil, and put the pan on the stove over medium heat. After adding the steak, continue cooking for another five minutes. Cook the fennel and shallots for seven minutes after adding them to the pan.
2. Mix in the pepper along with the bay leaf and thyme. Continue to cook for one more minute. The beef, together with the stock and the wine, should be added to the pan. Bring it up to a boil, then turn the heat down to a simmer. Cover, continuing to cook for another 45 minutes.
3. Include your mushrooms, onions, potatoes, and carrots in the dish. Continue cooking for another half hour, and your vegetables should be fork-tender at this point.
4. Before serving, remove the thyme sprigs and bay leaf from the dish. Sprinkle some chopped parsley on top.

Nutrition Info

- Calories: 244
- Protein: 21 Grams
- Fat: 8 Grams
- Carbs: 22.1 Grams
- Sodium: 587 mg
- Cholesterol: 125 mg

PORK CHOPS

Serves: 6 | Time: 30 Minutes

Ingredients:

- 2 Tablespoons Dijon Mustard
- 6 Pork Loin Chops, Center Cut
- 2 Teaspoons Olive Oil
- 1/3 Cup Wine Vinegar
- ¼ Cup Black Currant Jam
- 6 Orange Slices
- 1/8 Teaspoon Black Pepper

Directions:

1. To get started, take a bowl and combine your mustard and jam ingredients. Take out a skillet that won't stick, and then coat it in olive oil before setting it on a burner set to medium heat. After cooking the chops for five minutes on each side, spread one spoonful of the jam mixture on top of each one before serving.

2. Cover it, and let it cook for two minutes with the cover on. Place them on a platter intended for serving. Pour your wine vinegar into the same skillet, scrape out any browned bits, and stir everything thoroughly to deglaze the pan.
3. Pour this over your pork chops before serving. Before serving, garnish with slices of orange and ground black pepper.

Nutrition Info

- Calories: 265
- Protein: 25 Grams
- Fat: 6 Grams
- Carbs: 11 Grams
- Sodium: 120 mg
- Cholesterol: 22 mg

SPICY TOMATO SHRIMP

Serves: 6 | Time: 35 Minutes

Ingredients:

- ¾ lb. Shrimp, Uncooked, Peeled & Deveined
- 2 Tablespoons Tomato Paste
- ½ Teaspoon Garlic, Minced
- ½ Teaspoon Olive Oil
- ½ Teaspoons Water
- ½ Teaspoon Oregano, Chopped
- ½ Teaspoon Chipotle Chili Powder

Directions:

1. Before laying the shrimp aside, make sure to wash them and pat them dry. Bring a bowl to the table and start combining your tomato paste, water, chili powder, oil, oregano, and garlic in it.

2. Apply this all over the shrimp, making sure to coat them on both sides, and set them aside. Marinate for approximately twenty minutes or until you are ready to start the grilling process. After preheating a gas grill to a heat setting in the middle of the range, oil the cooking grate.

3. Position it so that it is six inches away from the source of the heat. Put the shrimp on skewers and cook them for four minutes on each side. To be served hot.

Nutrition Info

- Calories: 185
- Protein: 16.9 Grams
- Fat: 1 Gram
- Carbs: 12.4 Grams
- Sodium: 394 mg
- Cholesterol: 15 mg

BEEF STIR FRY

Serves: 4 | Time: 40 Minutes

Ingredients:

- 1 Head Broccoli Chopped into Florets
- 1 Red Bell Pepper, Sliced Thin
- ½ Cups Brown Rice
- Scallions, Sliced Thin
- Tablespoons Sesame Seeds
- ¼ Teaspoon Black Pepper
- lb. Flank Steak, Sliced Thin
- Tablespoons Canola Oil
- ¾ Cup Stir Fry Sauce

Directions:

1. To begin, bring the oil to temperature in a big wok set over medium-high heat. You should now add your steak and season it with pepper. Cook for a total of four minutes or until the bacon is crispy. Take it out of the skillet immediately.

2. Put the broccoli in the skillet. Turn the heat to high, and cook for about four minutes. Toss every once in a while. It should still have some crunch to it. After placing the steak back in the pan, pour the sauce over it. Please keep an eye on it and stir it every three minutes.
3. Garnish with sesame seeds and scallions. Serve over rice.

Nutrition Info

- Calories: 408
- Protein: 31 Grams
- Fat: 18 Grams
- Carbs: 36 Grams
- Sodium: 461 mg
- Cholesterol: 57 mg

SHRIMP AND CORN CHOWDER

Serves: 6 | Time: 50 Minutes

Ingredients:

- 2 Carrots, Peeled & Sliced
- 1 Yellow Onion, Sliced
- 3 Tablespoons Olive Oil
- 2 Celery Stalks, Diced
- 4 Baby Red Potatoes, Diced
- 4 Cloves Garlic, Peeled & Minced
- ¼ Cup All Purpose Flour
- 3 Cups Vegetable Stock, Unsalted
- ½ Cup Milk
- ¾ Teaspoon Sea Salt, Fine
- ¼ Teaspoon Black Pepper
- ¼ Teaspoon Cayenne Pepper
- 4Cups Corn Kernels Fresh

- 1lb. Shrimp, Peeled & Deveined
- 2 Scallions Sliced Thin

Directions:

1. Bring out a stockpot and start heating your oil over medium heat. When the oil is sufficiently hot, add the vegetables (carrots, celery, potatoes, and onions). Wait seven minutes before serving.
2. The vegetable ought to become more tender. First, give it a stir, then add the garlic. Continue to cook for one more minute. Create a roux with the flour, and then raise the temperature to medium-high. Mix it well while bringing it up to a low simmer. Make a point of whisking away any lumps that may have formed.
3. Mix in your milk along with the salt, pepper, and cayenne pepper. Allow it to simmer until it reaches the desired consistency. It should take roughly eight minutes to complete this task. Cook for another five minutes after adding the shrimp and corn to the pan. Divide between bowls to serve warm.

Nutrition Info

- Calories: 340
- Protein: 23 Grams
- Fat: 9 Grams
- Carbs: 45 Grams
- Sodium: 473 mg
- Cholesterol: 115 mg

LEEK AND CAULIFLOWER SOUP

Serves: 6 | Time: 40 Minutes

Ingredients:

- 1 Tablespoon Olive Oil
- 1 Leek, Trimmed & Sliced Thin
- 1 Yellow Onion, Peeled & Diced
- 1 Head Cauliflower, Chopped into Florets
- 3 Cloves Garlic, Minced
- 2 Tablespoons Thyme, Fresh & Chopped
- 1 Teaspoon Smoked Paprika
- 1 ¼ Teaspoon Sea Salt, Fine
- 1/4Teaspoon Ground Cayenne Pepper
- 1 Tablespoon Heavy Cream
- 3 Cups Vegetable Stock, Unsalted
- ½ Lemon, Juiced & Zested

Directions:

1. The cauliflower, leek, and onion should be added to the oil that has been heated in a stockpot over medium heat. Keep cooking for another five minutes or until the onion starts to become more tender.
2. Garlic, thyme, smoked paprika, salt, pepper, and cayenne pepper should all be added now. After adding the vegetable stock, bring the mixture to a simmer. Continue cooking for another fifteen minutes.
3. Your cauliflower needs to be cooked until it is very soft. Take the pan off the heat and mix in the cream, along with the lemon juice and lemon zest. To achieve a smooth purée, use an immersion blender and serve warm.

Nutrition Info

- Calories: 92
- Protein: 5 Grams
- Fat: 4 Grams
- Carbs: 13 Grams
- Sodium: 556 mg
- Cholesterol: 3 mg

EASY BEEF BRISKET

Serves: 4 | Time: 3 Hours 10 Minutes

Ingredients:

- 1 Teaspoon Thyme
- 4 Cloves Garlic, Peeled & Smashed
- 1½ Cups Onion, chopped
- 2½ lbs. Beef Brisket, Chopped
- 1 Tablespoon Olive Oil
- ¼ Teaspoon Black Pepper
- 14.5 Ounces of Tomatoes & Liquid, Canned
- ¼ Cup Red Wine Vinegar
- 1 Cup Beef Stock, Low Sodium

Directions:

1. After preheating the oven to 350 degrees, prepare a Dutch oven by greasing it with one tablespoon of oil. Put it in a heat setting that is just medium. Add in your pepper and brisket.

2. After it has reached the desired level of browning, transfer the brisket to a plate. Place the onions in the pot and sauté them until they are a deep golden color. Before adding the stock, vinegar, and tomatoes, stir in the garlic and thyme that you have prepared and continue cooking for another minute.

3. Continue cooking until it reaches a boil, and then stir in your brisket once more. Turn the heat down to a simmer and continue cooking in the oven for another three hours or until the meat is soft.

Nutrition Info

- Calories: 299
- Protein: 10.2 Grams
- Fat: 9 Grams
- Carbs: 21.4 Grams
- Sodium: 372 mg
- Cholesterol: 101 mg

COCONUT SHRIMP

Serves: 4 | Time: 25 Minutes

Ingredients:

- ¼ Cup Coconut, Sweetened
- ½ Teaspoon Sea Salt, Fine
- ¼ Cup Panko Breadcrumbs
- ½ Cup Coconut Milk
- 12 Large Shrimp, Peeled & Deveined

Directions:

1. First, bring a baking pan to the table while your oven preheats to 375 degrees. After spraying it with cooking spray, you should then set it aside.
2. Using a food processor, grind the panko together with the coconut and the salt. This mixture should be added to a bowl, and the coconut milk should be poured into a separate bowl. After coating the shrimp in the coconut mixture, dredge it in the panko mixture to ensure that it is thoroughly coated.

3. Place the shrimp that have been coated on the pan for baking, and bake them for fifteen minutes to be served hot.

Nutrition Info

- Calories: 249
- Protein: 35 Grams
- Fat: 1.7 Grams
- Carbs: 1.8 Grams
- Sodium: 79 mg
- Cholesterol: 78 mg

ASIAN SALMON

Serves: 2 | Time: 30 Minutes

Ingredients:

- 1Cup Fresh Fruit, Diced
- ¼ Teaspoon Black Pepper
- 2 Salmon Fillets, 4 Ounces Each
- ¼ Teaspoon Sesame Oil
- 1 Teaspoon Soy Sauce, Low Sodium
- 2 Cloves Garlic, Minced
- ½ Cup Pineapple Juice, Sugar-Free

Directions:

1. To begin, get a bowl ready and combine your garlic, soy sauce, ginger, and pineapple juice in it. Put the fish in the dough and make sure it's well covered with it. It sits for an hour in the marinade.
2. After thirty minutes, give the fillets a flip and then preheat the oven to 375 degrees. Take out some squares of aluminum foil and put some cooking spray on them. Place a salmon fillet on top of each square, then sprinkle with pepper and garnish with diced fruit and sesame oil.

3. After securing the fish with the folded aluminum foil using a sealant, set the fish on the baking sheet. Bake for 10 minutes per side before serving.

Nutrition Info

- Calories: 247
- Protein: 27 Grams
- Fat: 7 Grams
- Carbs: 19 Grams
- Sodium: 350 mg
- Cholesterol: 120 mg

BASIL HALIBUT

Serve: 4 | Time: 30 Minutes

Ingredients:

- 4 Halibut Fillets, 4 Ounces Each
- 2 Teaspoons Olive Oil
- 1 Tablespoon Garlic, Minced
- 2 Tomatoes, Diced
- 2 Tablespoons Basil, Fresh & Chopped
- 1 Teaspoon Oregano, Fresh & Chopped

Directions:

1. First, preheat the oven to 350 degrees. Then take out a pan that is 9 inches by 13 inches. Spray some cooking spray on it and wipe it down.
2. Put the tomato, basil, olive oil, and oregano in a bowl and toss everything together. Pour this over the fish that is now cooking in the pan. Cook for a total of twelve minutes. Your fish ought to have a flaky texture.

Nutrition Info

- Calories: 128

- Protein: 21 Grams
- Fat: 4 Grams
- Carbs: 3 Grams
- Sodium: 81 mg
- Cholesterol: 55 mg

Chapter 5 Snacks

PESTO MUSHROOMS

Serves: 10 | Time: 25 Minutes

Ingredients:

- 20 Cremini Mushrooms, Washed & Stemmed

Toppings:

- 1 ½ Cups Panko Breadcrumbs
- ¼ Cup Butter, Melted
- 3 Tablespoons Parsley, Fresh & Chopped

Filling:

- 2 Cups Basil Leaves, Fresh & Chopped
- ¼ Cup Parmesan Cheese, Grated Fresh
- 2 Tablespoons Pumpkin Seeds
- 1 Tablespoon Garlic, Fresh
- 1Tablespoon Olive Oil

- 2 Teaspoons Lemon Juice, Fresh
- ½ Teaspoon Sea Salt, Fine

Directions:

1. After preheating the oven to 350 degrees, put the mushrooms on a baking sheet so that the caps are facing upward. To begin preparing the topping, obtain a bowl and mix the butter, panko, and parsley together in it.
2. In a blender, put your pumpkin seeds, cheese, garlic, oil, basil, and lemon juice, and then blend. Blend until everything is thoroughly incorporated. Before proceeding to add the panko mixture on top, the mushrooms should be stuffed with the basil paste. Bake the caps for fifteen minutes after pressing this mixture into them.
3. Before serving them warm, they should turn a golden brown color.

Nutrition Info

- Calories: 159
- Protein: 2 Grams
- Fat: 3 Grams
- Carbs: 4 Grams
- Sodium: 63 mg
- Cholesterol: 8 mg

LEMON GREEN BEANS WITH ALMONDS

Serves: 4 | Time: 30 Minutes

Ingredients:

- ¼ Cup Parmesan Cheese, Grated Fine
- ¼ Cup Almonds, Sliced
- ¼ Teaspoon Black Pepper
- 1/8 Teaspoon Sea Salt, Fine
- 1 Lemon, Juiced & Zested
- 2 Tablespoons Olive Oil
- 1 lb. Green Beans, Trimmed

Directions:

1. To blanch your green beans, bring a saucepan of water to a boil and then cook them for three minutes.
2. After placing them in a bowl filled with ice water for three minutes, remove them from the basin and drain them. Warm your olive oil in a skillet over medium heat. After five minutes, or until they have a light browning, add your green beans and continue to sauté.

3. After you have added your lemon juice, continue to let it cook for another two minutes. Add a little salt and pepper before serving. It can then be served with lemon zest, parmesan, and almonds after being transferred to a serving dish.

Nutrition Info

- Calories: 162
- Protein: 6 Grams
- Fat: 11 Grams
- Carbs: 10 Grams
- Sodium: 132 mg
- Cholesterol: 0 mg

SWEET AND SAVORY BRUSSELS SPROUTS

Serves: 6 | Time: 30 Minutes

Ingredients:

- ¼ Cup Walnuts, Chopped
- 2 Tablespoons Olive Oil
- 2 lbs. Brussel Sprouts, Trimmed & Halved
- ¼ Teaspoon Black Pepper
- ¼ Teaspoon Sea Salt, Fine
- 1/8 Teaspoon Crushed Red Pepper Flakes
- 1Tablespoon Maple Syrup, Pure
- 2Tablespoons Dijon Mustard

Directions:

1. Toast your walnuts for two minutes in a dry skillet that has been preheated and placed over medium heat. First, they should get quick toasting, and then you should put them in a little bowl.

2. After bringing the olive oil to a simmer in a skillet over medium heat, add the Brussels sprouts to the pan. Keep stirring it every so often while it's cooking for ten minutes. They should be lightly browned and easily cut with a fork. Add some salt, black pepper, and crushed red pepper. After you have combined the Dijon mustard and the maple syrup in a bowl using a whisk, pour the mixture into the pan.

3. Stir the ingredients together thoroughly, then bring them to a low simmer. Place this in a dish, and then sprinkle the top with the toasted walnuts.

Nutrition Info

- Calories: 151
- Protein: 6 Grams
- Fat: 8 Grams
- Carbs: 16 Grams
- Sodium: 255 mg
- Cholesterol: 0 mg

CARAMELIZED SWEET POTATOES

Serves: 4 | Time: 55 Minutes

Ingredients:

- 2 Sweet potatoes, Cut into ½ Inch Wedges
- 2 Tablespoons Canola Oil
- ¼ Teaspoon Black Pepper
- ¼ Teaspoon Sea Salt, Fine

Directions:

1. After you have brought the temperature in your oven up to 450 degrees, prepare a baking sheet by lining it with a wire rack.
2. Spray some cooking spray on your wire rack, and then set it aside. Coat your sweet potatoes in oil, then season them with salt and pepper, and finally, space them out on the rack so that they have an inch between each other.

3. Bake for thirty-five to forty-five minutes, depending on the size. Adjust the oven to low broil and continue cooking for another four minutes. The edges ought to have a toasty appearance and be served hot.

Nutrition Info

- Calories: 111
- Protein: 1 Gram
- Fat: 7 Grams
- Carbs: 12 Grams
- Sodium: 166 mg
- Cholesterol: 0 mg

VEGETABLE AND POLENTA DISH

Serves: 4 | Time: 1 Hour

Ingredients:

- 2 Tablespoons Parmesan Cheese, Grated
- 1 Cup Zucchini, Sliced
- 1 Cup Broccoli Florets, Chopped
- 1 Cup Onions, Sliced
- 1 Cup Mushrooms, Fresh & Sliced
- ½ Teaspoon Oregano, Fresh & Chopped
- 1 Teaspoon Basil, Fresh & Chopped
- ½ Teaspoon Rosemary, Fresh & Chopped
- 1 Cup Polenta, Ground Coarsely
- 4 Cups water
- 1 Teaspoon Garlic, Chopped

Directions:

1. First, preheat the oven to 350 degrees. Then spray a baking dish that holds three quarts with cooking spray.
2. Combine the polenta, garlic, and water in a mixing bowl. Wait forty minutes before moving on to the next step, which is to heat a skillet that has been greased to a medium temperature. After another five minutes of simmering, throw in your mushrooms and onions. First, bring the kettle of water to a boil, and then place the steamer basket within.
3. Put the zucchini and broccoli in the steamer basket, cover it, and steam for three minutes. Cook the polenta in the oven together with the steamed vegetables, then top with cheese and fresh herbs to be served hot.

Nutrition Info

- Calories: 178
- Protein: 6 Grams
- Fat: 1 Gram
- Carbs: 22 Grams
- Sodium: 326 mg
- Cholesterol: 14 mg

ROSEMARY POTATO SKINS

Serves: 2 | Time: 1 Hour 10 Minutes

Ingredients:

- 2 Russet Potatoes
- Butter Flavored Cooking Spray
- 1 Tablespoon Rosemary, Fresh & Minced
- 1/8 Teaspoon Black Pepper

Directions:

1. After preheating the oven to 375 degrees, prick the potatoes all over with a fork. Put them on a baking sheet. Bake them in the oven for a full hour or until they are crispy.
2. After allowing them to cool for the appropriate amount of time, split them in half lengthwise. Remove the pulp using a spoon and leave a shell that is 1/8 of an inch thick.
3. The shells should be brushed with melted butter and then seasoned with pepper and rosemary. Keep the flesh aside for use in another dish or at another time.
4. Wait an additional five minutes after the last baking time before serving.

Nutrition Info

- Calories: 167
- Protein: 7.6 Grams
- Fat: 0 Grams
- Carbs: 27 Grams
- Sodium: 119 mg
- Cholesterol: 20 mg

SQUASH FRIES

Serves: 4 | Time: 25 Minutes

Ingredients:

- 1 Tablespoon Rosemary, Fresh & Chopped
- 1 Tablespoon Thyme, Fresh & Chopped
- 1 Tablespoon Olive Oil
- 1 Butternut Squash
- ½ Teaspoon Sea Salt, Fine

Directions:

1. First, bring a baking sheet to the table, and then preheat the oven to 425 degrees. Lubricate it. After peeling it, slice the squash into pieces that are half an inch wide and three inches long.
2. Place the pieces in a bowl, then add the salt, thyme, oil, and rosemary and mix to combine. Your squash should be spread out on the baking sheet and put in the oven for 10 minutes.

3. Turn the mixture over and bake for an additional five minutes. They ought to have a golden brown color.

Nutrition Info

- Calories: 62
- Protein: 11 Grams
- Fat: 2 Grams
- Carbs: 11 Grams
- Sodium: 38 mg
- Cholesterol: 1 mg

VEGETABLE KEBABS

Serves: 2 | Time: 55 Minutes

Ingredients:

- 1 Zucchini, Sliced into pieces
- 1 Red Onion, Quartered
- 1 Green bell Pepper, Cut into 4 Pieces
- 8 Button Mushrooms
- 8 Cherry Tomatoes
- ½ Cup Italian Dressing, Fat-Free
- 1 Red Bell Pepper, Cut into 4 Pieces
- ½ Cup Brown Rice
- 1 Cup Water

Directions:

1. Marinate the zucchini, mushrooms, onion, peppers, and tomatoes for ten minutes in your Italian dressing by tossing them in the bowl with the dressing and allowing them to sit for the same amount of time.

2. Make sure that they have a thick coating. In a saucepan, bring the water and rice to a boil. Then lower the heat to a simmer. Cook the rice, covered, for thirty minutes or until it reaches the desired doneness.

3. Start by preheating your grill to medium before you do anything else. Spray some cooking spray on the grilling rack, and then arrange it so that it is four inches from the heat source. Each skewer should have two slices of tomato, two slices of mushroom, two slices of zucchini, one wedge of onion, one slice of green pepper, and one slice of red pepper.

4. Grill for five minutes per side. Serve while the rice is still hot.

Nutrition Info

- Calories: 335
- Protein: 8.8 Grams
- Fat: 8.2 Grams
- Carbs: 67 Grams
- Sodium: 516 mg
- Cholesterol: 110 mg

Chapter 6 Dessert

TOASTED ALMOND AMBROSIA

Serves: 2 | Time: 30 Minutes

Ingredients:

- ½ Cup Almonds, Slivered
- ½ Cup Coconut, Shredded & Unsweetened
- 3 Cups Pineapple, Cubed
- 5 Oranges, Segment
- 1Banana, Halved Lengthwise, Peeled & Sliced
- 2Red Apples, Cored & Diced
- 2 Tablespoons Cream Sherry
- Mint Leaves, Fresh to Garnish

Directions:

1. First, get your oven up to temperature (325 degrees), and then get a baking sheet ready. Roast your almonds for 10 minutes, ensuring that they are evenly distributed on the baking sheet.
2. Place them on a platter, and then use the same baking sheet to toast your coconut. Broil the bread for 10 minutes. In a bowl, combine the sherry, banana, oranges, apples, and pineapple that you have.

3. The mixture should be divided among the serving bowls, and then coconut and almonds should be sprinkled on top. Before serving, sprinkle some mint on top.

Nutrition Info

- Calories: 177
- Protein: 3.4 Grams
- Fat: 4.9 Grams
- Carbs: 36 Grams
- Sodium: 13 mg
- Cholesterol: 11 mg

APPLE DUMPLINGS

Serves: 4 | Time: 40 Minutes

Ingredients:

<u>Dough:</u>

- 1 Tablespoon Butter
- 1 Teaspoon Honey, Raw
- 1Cup Whole Wheat Flour
- 2Tablespoons Buckwheat Flour
- 2 Tablespoons Rolled Oats
- 2 Tablespoons Brandy or Apple Liquor

<u>Filling:</u>

- 2 Tablespoons Honey, Raw
- 1 Teaspoon Nutmeg
- 6 Tart Apples, Sliced Thin
- 1 Lemon, Zested

103

Directions:

1. Preheat the oven to 350°F. To make a crumbly mixture, get out of your food processor and blend your butter, flour, honey, and oats until the mixture becomes crumbly. After adding your brandy or apple liquor, continue pounding the mixture until it comes together to create a dough.

2. After two hours, remove it from the refrigerator and remove the plastic wrap before serving. Toss your apples with the lemon zest, honey, and nutmeg until they are evenly coated. Your dough should be rolled out into a sheet that is about a quarter of an inch thick. After cutting out circles with a diameter of eight inches, place each one in a muffin tin that has been oiled. First, the dough needs to be pressed down, and then the apple mixture may be stuffed within.

3. Fold the edges inward and squeeze them shut to secure them. Check to see that they have an adequate seal. Bake for thirty minutes or until the topping is golden brown, and then drizzle with honey.

Nutrition Info

- Calories: 178
- Protein: 5 Grams
- Fat: 4 Grams
- Carbs: 23 Grams
- Sodium: 562 mg
- Cholesterol: 61 mg

APRICOT BISCUIT

Serves: 4 | Time: 50 Minutes

Ingredients:

- 2 Tablespoons Honey, Dark
- 2 Tablespoons Olive Oil
- ½ Teaspoon Almond Extract
- ¼ Cup Almonds, Chopped Roughly
- 2/3 Cup Apricots, Dried
- 2 Tablespoons Milk, 1% & Low Fat
- 2 Eggs, Beaten Lightly
- ¾ Cup Whole Wheat Flour
- ¾ Cup All Purpose Flour
- ¼ Cup Brown Sugar, Packed Firm
- 1 Teaspoon Baking Powder

Directions:

1. First, make sure your oven is heated to 350 degrees. Then, mix your baking powder, brown sugar, and flour together in a bowl. Mix together your milk, honey, canola oil, eggs, and almond essence in a bowl.

2. Perform thorough mixing until a smooth dough is formed. Combine the apricots and almonds by folding them in. Place the dough on a piece of plastic wrap, and then roll it out into a rectangle that is twelve inches in length and three inches wide. Put the dough in a single layer on a baking sheet. Bake it for twenty-five minutes.

3. It ought to get a golden-brown color. After allowing it to cool, slice it into pieces that are about half an inch thick, and then return it to the oven for another fifteen minutes. It needs to have a crisp texture.

Nutrition Info

- Calories: 291
- Protein: 2 Grams
- Fat: 2 Grams
- Carbs: 12 Grams
- Sodium: 123 mg
- Cholesterol: 21 mg

APPLE AND BERRY COBBLER

Serves: 4 | Time: 40 Minutes

Ingredients:

Filling:

- 1 Cup Blueberries, Fresh
- 2 Cups Apples, Chopped1 Cup Raspberries, Fresh
- 2 Tablespoons Brown Sugar
- 1 Teaspoon Lemon Zest
- 2 Teaspoon Lemon Juice, Fresh
- ½ Teaspoon Ground Cinnamon
- 1 ½ Tablespoons Corn Starch

Topping:

- ¾ Cup Whole Wheat Pastry Flour
- 1 ½ Tablespoon Brown Sugar
- ½ Teaspoon Vanilla Extract, Pure
- ¼ Cup Soy Milk

- ¼ Teaspoon Sea Salt, Fine
- 1 Egg White

Directions:

1. Prepare six individual ramekins and preheat the oven to 350 degrees. Spray some cooking spray on them to grease them. In a bowl, combine the lemon juice, lemon zest, blueberries, sugar, cinnamon, raspberries, and apples.
2. Mix until everything is well combined. Mix in your cornstarch and continue to stir until it has dissolved completely. Your egg white should be beaten in a separate bowl while you whisk it together with sugar, vanilla, soy milk, and pastry flour.
3. The berry mixture should be distributed evenly among the ramekins, and then the vanilla topping should be added on top. Place the ramekins you will be using on a baking sheet and bake them for half an hour. Before serving, make sure the top is browned to a golden color.

Nutrition Info

- Calories: 131
- Protein: 7.2 Grams
- Fat: 1 Gram
- Carbs: 13.8 Grams
- Sodium: 14 mg
- Cholesterol: 2.1 mg

MIXED FRUIT COMPOTE CUPS

Serves: 2 | Time: 15 Minutes

Ingredients:

- 1 ¼ Cup Water
- ½ Cup Orange juice
- 12 Ounces Mixed Dried Fruit
- 1 Teaspoon Ground Cinnamon
- ¼ Teaspoon Ground Ginger
- ¼ Teaspoon Ground Nutmeg
- 4 Cups Vanilla Frozen Yogurt, Fat-Free

Directions:

1. In a saucepan, combine the ginger, nutmeg, cinnamon, orange juice, and water, then stir in the dried fruit.
2. Ten minutes of cooking time should pass with the lid on and the heat set to medium. Take off the lid, then continue cooking for another 10 minutes.
3. Place some frozen yogurt in individual serving cups, then sprinkle the fruit mixture over the top.

Nutrition Info

- Calories: 228
- Protein: 9.1 Grams
- Fat: 5.7 Grams
- Carbs: 12.4 Grams
- Sodium: 114 mg
- Cholesterol: 15 mg

OATMEAL COOKIES

Serves: 24 | Time: 25 Minutes

Ingredients:

- 1½ Cups Creamy Peanut Butter, All Natural
- ½ Cup Dark Brown Sugar
- 2 Eggs, Large
- 1 Cup Old Fashioned Rolled Oats
- 1 Teaspoon Baking Soda
- ½ Teaspoon Sea Salt, Fine
- ½ Cup Dark Chocolate Chips

Directions:

1. To begin, set the oven temperature to 350 degrees and take out a baking sheet. Prepare a sheet of parchment paper to line your baking sheet. Prepare a bowl for the peanut

butter to be whipped into using an electric mixer, and do so until it is completely smooth. Keep mixing the mixture while gradually adding the brown sugar.

2. Continue to beat the mixture while you gradually add in the eggs, one at a time, until the eggs are well mixed and the mixture is fluffy. Mix in the oats, then add the salt and baking soda. Stop the mixer and gently incorporate the dark chocolate chunks into the mixture.

3. Your cookie dough should be spaced out on the baking sheet by about two inches, and it should be baked for around eight to ten minutes.

Nutrition Info

- Calories: 152
- Protein: 4 Grams
- Fat: 10 Grams
- Carbs: 12 Grams
- Sodium: 131 mg
- Cholesterol: 18 mg

ALMOND AND APRICOT CRISP

Serves: 4 | Time: 35 Minutes

Ingredients:

- 1 Teaspoon Olive Oil
- 1 lb. Apricot, Halved & Pits Removed
- ½ Cup Almonds, Chopped
- 1 Tablespoons Oats
- 1 Teaspoon Anise Seeds
- 2 Tablespoons Honey, Raw

Directions:

1. First, preheat the oven to 350 degrees. Then grease a pie plate that is nine inches in diameter with olive oil.
2. After they have been chopped, your apricots should be added, and you should distribute them in an even layer. To finish, sprinkle some anise seeds, oats, and almonds on top. Honey should be drizzled on top, and the dish should be baked for another 25 minutes. It ought to get a golden-brown color.

Nutrition Info

- Calories: 149
- Protein: 3 Grams
- Fat: 11.9 Grams
- Carbs: 18.8 Grams
- Sodium: 79 mg
- Cholesterol: 78 mg

BLUEBERRY APPLE COBBLER

Serves: 4 | Time: 40 Minutes

Ingredients:

- 2 Tablespoons Cornstarch
- 2 Tablespoons Sugar
- 1 Tablespoon Lemon Juice, Fresh
- 2 Apples, Large, Peeled, Cored & Sliced
- 1 Teaspoon Ground Cinnamon
- 12 Ounces Blueberries, Fresh

Toppings:

- ¼ Teaspoon Sea Salt, Fine
- ¾ Cup All Purpose Flour
- ¾ Cup Whole Wheat Flour
- 2 Tablespoons Sugar
- 1 ½ Teaspoons Baking Powder
- 4 Tablespoons Margarine, Cold & Chopped
- ½ Cup Milk, Fat-Free

- 1 Teaspoon Vanilla Extract, Pure

Directions:

1. After preheating the oven to 400 degrees, take out a baking pan that is nine inches in diameter. Spray some cooking spray on it to grease it. Before adding the cornstarch, sugar, and cinnamon, you should first combine the lemon juice and apples in a bowl.
2. Check to see that it is coated uniformly. Throw in the blueberries, and then use the remaining mixture to cover the bottom of the baking dish. Take out a bowl and start combining the baking powder, sugar, both flours, and salt in it. The margarine should be cut into pieces and then mixed in until it creates a mixture that is crumbly. After adding the milk and vanilla extract, thoroughly combine the ingredients to make a moist dough. Perform the kneading with floured hands.
3. It should be rolled out into a rectangle that is a half-inch thick. Using a cookie cutter, cut the dough into the shapes that appeal to you the most. You can cut more cookies out of the scraps that are left over. Put this on top of your apple mixture until it is thoroughly covered, then bake it for half an hour before presenting it to your guests.

Nutrition Info

- Calories: 288
- Protein: 6 Grams
- Fat: 6.2 Grams
- Carbs: 48 Grams
- Sodium: 176 mg
- Cholesterol: 120 mg

Conclusion

At this point, you are fully equipped with the knowledge necessary to reap the benefits of following the DASH diet. There is no reason to just accept hypertension as something you have to live with, but you should keep in mind that even with this change in diet, you will still need any medication that has been prescribed to you by your doctor, and you will also need to exercise regularly in order to maintain your health and reap the full benefits of this dietary change. It is possible to stop hypertension with a dietary strategy, especially when combined with regular exercise and balanced nutrition. Don't let hypertension run your life. Get a grip on things by beginning with your eating habits and working your way up from there.

Made in the USA
Monee, IL
21 February 2023

28408668R00070